EGMONT

We bring stories to life

First published in Great Britain in 2014
by Egmont UK Limited,
The Yellow Building, 1 Nicholas Road, London W11 4AN.

Writer: Kate Graham
Designer: Jeanette Ryall

© 2014 Disney Enterprises, Inc.

ISBN 978 1 4052 71318
57315/1
Printed in Italy

This special
Sofia the First
Holiday Annual belongs
to *Princess*

Meet Sofia   8

Meet Sofia's Family   10

Welcome to the Castle   12

Story: Our Royal Debut – Part 1   14

Tiara Trouble   18

Posters   19

Tidy-up Time   21

Meet Clover the Rabbit   22

Princess-in-Training   24

Story: Our Royal Debut – Part 2   26

Meet Robin the Robin   30

Castle Maze   32

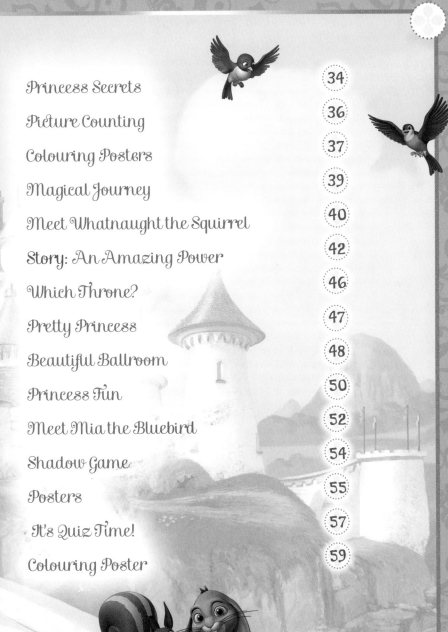

Princess Secrets 34

Picture Counting 36

Colouring Posters 37

Magical Journey 39

Meet Whatnaught the Squirrel ... 40

Story: An Amazing Power 42

Which Throne? 46

Pretty Princess 47

Beautiful Ballroom 48

Princess Fun 50

Meet Mia the Bluebird 52

Shadow Game 54

Posters 55

It's Quiz Time! 57

Colouring Poster 59

Meet Sofia

I'm new to being a princess.
Read my story here!

Use the little picture above to help you colour Sofia's dress.

All About Me

Once upon a time … I led a simple life with my mother, who worked in the village shoe shop. Then, my mum and King Roland fell in love and got married. That made me a princess!

 I live:
In the castle of Enchancia. My bedroom is HUGE!

 I wear:
A lilac princess dress and a matching tiara. (Actually, I have six tiaras!)

 I like:
Adventures, making new friends, being a princess – although I have a lot to learn about that.

I love:
My mum most of all. I'm getting to know and love my new, royal family, too.

My best friends:
Jade and Ruby, who I've known since long before I became a princess. Now, Clover the rabbit is my best friend, too.

My school:
Royal Prep Academy. Only princes and princesses go there.

 My favourite word:
Why? I'm always asking questions!

My secret:
My magical amulet necklace gives me special powers!

Love Sofia x

Meet Sofia's Family

My family has suddenly grown! Let me introduce you.

Miranda, Queen of Enchancia

My mother was once a village shoemaker. She met the king when he needed a new pair of royal slippers.

King Roland II

King Roland is a great king and he's kind, too. He was very happy when I accepted him as my new dad!

Princess Amber

Amber played tricks on me at first. But now we have fun. She gives me princess tips and even arranged a royal sleepover. That was so cool!

Prince James

This is Amber's twin brother, James. He's really nice and always helps me. He's a lot of fun, too.

The Three Good Fairies

Flora, Fauna and Merryweather are the headmistresses at Royal Prep. They aren't part of my family, but they are a VERY important part of my new life. I love going to school!

Follow the trail from the fairies to see who Sofia loves the most!

Answer: Sofia loves her mother the most.

Welcome to the Castle

Sofia is excited to have the castle of Enchancia as her new home. She has lots of exploring to do!

1

Can you work out which missing piece goes where to complete this lovely scene?

a

b

c

d

e

f

2

Which jigsaw piece doesn't belong in the picture?

Our Royal Debut

1 Today is an amazing day! Mum and I are leaving our village to move into a beautiful castle. Now she's King Roland II's wife and the Queen of Enchancia.

2 And I'm now a princess ... Princess Sofia the First!

HI! I'M SOFIA!

3 The trouble is, I don't really know much about being a princess and I'm sure I'll never be as perfect as my royal stepsister, Princess Amber.

4 I have never had to do a royal wave. I don't know when to curtsy! "Just be yourself and you'll be fine," Mum says. But how can I be myself and be a princess at the same time?

5 "We're having a ball in your honour and we'll dance the first waltz together," King Roland tells me. Then he gives me a welcome-to-the-family gift ...

6 ... a precious necklace called the Amulet of Avalor. I hope it can help me dance like a princess, or I shall be in trouble at the ball!

7 Luckily, there's a dance class at my new school, Royal Prep Academy, where all princes and princesses go.

8 Amber even lends me a pair of very special shoes. Isn't that fantastic? I think she's starting to like me!

Will Sofia learn to dance in time for the ball? You can find out on page 26.

Tiara Trouble

These tiaras may look the same, but one is different – and it belongs to Sofia! Can you help her find it?

1

a

b

c

d

2

Is Sofia's amulet yellow?

Yes   No

18

A princess
is kind to
animals.

Cut along here

Tidy-up Time

Oh dear, Sofia's new princess things have got in a bit of a muddle. Can you help her sort them out?

paintbrush

teacup

amulet

tiara

doll

doll

paints

teapot

1

Draw lines to link the items that go together, so that Sofia can tidy up quickly.

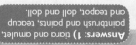

21

Meet Clover the Rabbit

Clover is always thinking about food. He loves snacking on carrots!

He loves ...

Clover has a very big heart and he's devoted to Sofia. He will do anything for her.

In charge

Although Clover is leader of the woodland animals, each of the creatures helps Sofia in their own way.

1

What colour are Clover's eyes?

blue · brown

Clover needs some
bunny colours.
Remember to give
his floppy ears
black tips!

Clover says:
I like Sofia because she's
kind and loving to everyone.

Princess-in-Training

It's the start of the school day at Royal Prep Academy and Sofia has a lot to learn!

Art

1

In her Art lesson Sofia painted a royal vase. How many paintbrushes did she use?

Writing

2

What is Sofia going to write in her Writing lesson? Trace over the letters and find out!

Manners

3

Sofia will pour a cup of tea the princess way in her Manners lesson. Circle what is on the tea table that should not be there.

Our Royal Debut

9 Oh dear! Amber has tricked me. The shoes are under a magic spell and make me spin around and around until I fall down. Even worse, I still don't know how to waltz and the ball is tonight!

10 Then I remember Cedric, the Royal Sorcerer. I ask him to help me, and he writes down some magic words. If I recite them, I'll waltz like a real princess!

11 The King – um, I mean my new dad – asks me to dance when I enter the ballroom. But the spell doesn't work. My feet don't start to dance at all! Instead, everyone falls asleep! "Help!" I cry and then my amulet glows ...

Cinderella

12 ... and to my surprise Cinderella appears! "When a princess is in trouble, another one always comes to help," she says. "I think your new sister can help you reverse the spell. Perhaps you should give Amber a second chance."

13   Amber is worried that everyone will like me more than her. "No way," I say, giving her a hug. I explain what happened with Cedric's spell. We search his workshop until we find a counterspell.

14 "Wait! I owe you a dance lesson!" Amber tells me. Hooray! Now Amber trusts me and I can dance, too. I know we're now ever-true sisters and friends!

15) The new spell awakes everyone in the ballroom. "You dance wonderfully, Sofia!" Dad says. "I'm proud of you. You'll be a great princess." Amber is smiling at me, too. I think I'm going to fit into this royal family after all!

The End

Meet Robin the Robin

Robin is a songbird with a lovely singing voice.

Wise friend

She's the wisest of all Sofia's animal friends and gives the young princess sensible advice.

Beady eye

Robin keeps a close eye on Clover. She makes sure he doesn't get too gruff or bossy.

1

Trace over the letters to write Robin's name.

Robin

Castle Maze

Sofia has been visiting Cedric the Sorcerer in his workshop. Now she wants to join Amber and James in the castle garden.

1

Can you help Sofia find her way through the maze to reach the garden?

Start →

Finish

2

How many ravens can you count? Make sure Sofia doesn't bump into any of them as she goes!

33

Princess Secrets

Amber is sharing her princess secrets with Sofia. Can you see five differences between the two pictures opposite?

Colour in an amulet every time you find a difference.

Picture Counting

1, 2, 3 ... It's time to help Sofia practise her counting!

1

Can you find three pictures of James?

Yes   No

2

Mia is looking for Robin. Can you spot her?

3

How many bags can you count?

Brighten up headmistresses Flora, Fauna and Merryweather with your colouring pens.

Colour in this picture of Sofia in princess school for top marks!

Magical Journey

Sofia flies through the sky to school, in a carriage driven by winged horses!

Biggest

Smallest

a

b

c

d

Arrange the carriages in order of size, starting with the biggest.

39

Meet Whatnaught the Squirrel

Whatnaught grins and giggles all day long, but he's much more than just a happy squirrel.

Silent squirrel

Whatnaught is actually very, very clever. No one knows this because he never speaks!

Best friends

Whatnaught and Clover get along very well together. The squirrel is smiley and sweet, even when Clover is a bit grumpy.

1 Which creature comes next in the sequence? Add S for Squirrel or R for Rabbit in the end circle.

Colour in
Whatnaught
to keep him
smiling!

Whatnaught thinks:
I like Sofia because she's
adventurous and curious.

An Amazing Power

 It's break time at Royal Prep Academy and we are having fun in the playground. My stepbrother James invites me to take a ride on the magic swing. Wow! I can't wait! But the swing swings itself faster and faster and then ... **Splash!**

2 I end up in the fountain! I walk away quickly, feeling silly and wanting my mother. Then I hear chirping coming from underneath a tree. It's a scared baby bird! "It's all right, I can help," I tell him.

3 When the mummy bird sees her lost baby, she starts chirping, too. "Here you go, just the two of you, the way it should be," I say. Suddenly my amulet glows! How come? It has never done this before.

4 As I walk back to school, I hear someone saying "Thank you!" It can't be the birds, I'm sure. But the next morning I open my eyes and there's a rabbit on my bed! "Shh, I'm Clover," he says. I can understand him!

5 There are also two birds named Robin and Mia, and a squirrel named Whatnaught. They are surprised too, because I understand what they say! I think that the amulet must be magic. Because I helped the baby bird, it rewarded me with the power to talk with animals!

6 "Time to dress up, Sofia," says Mia. "Animals have always helped princesses," explains Clover. Isn't it great? I'm so happy my amulet gave me this power. I'm on the right path to becoming a good princess!

The End

Which Throne?

Special visitors are coming to Enchancia. The royal family must sit on their thrones to welcome them.

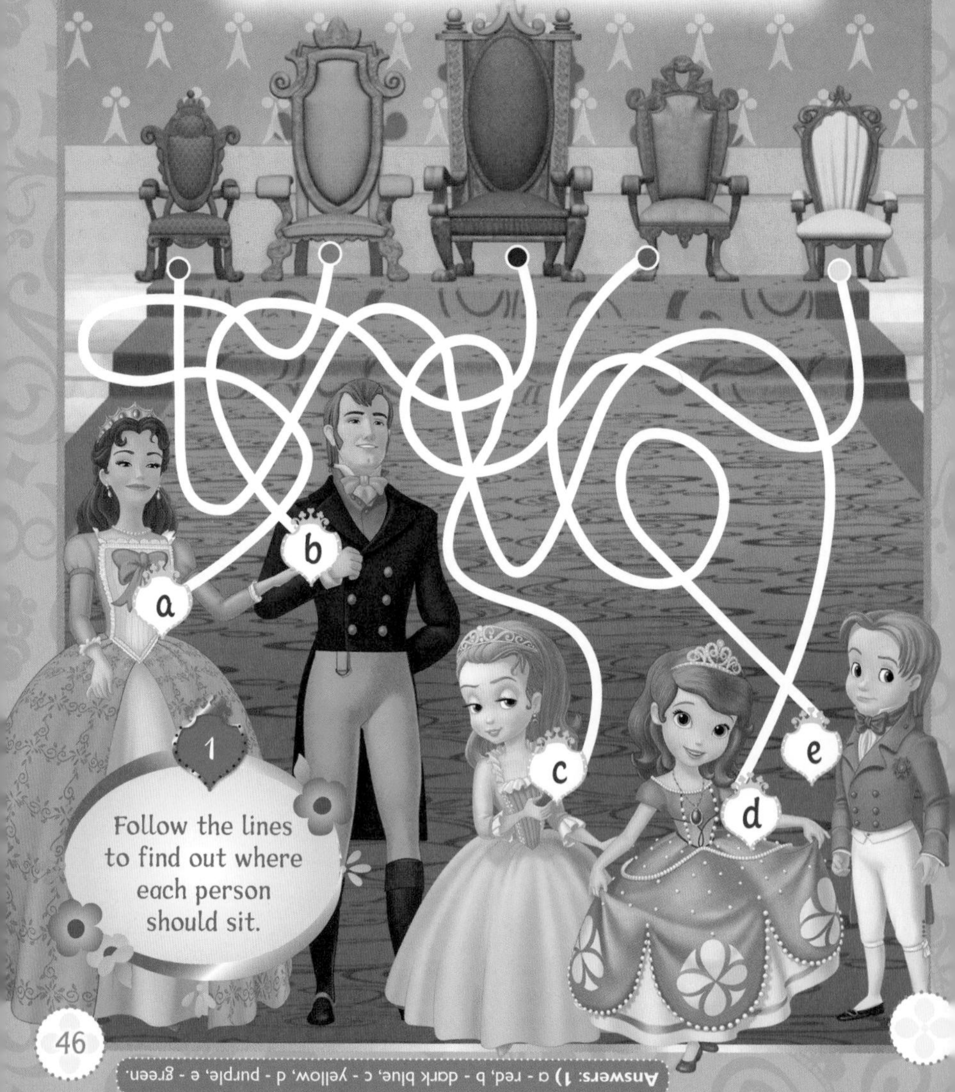

1

Follow the lines to find out where each person should sit.

a

b

c

d

e

Pretty Princess

Join the dots to complete the sweet picture, then colour it in.

Beautiful Ballroom

The guests will soon arrive at the royal ball. Even though Sofia is nervous about dancing, she is feeling like a true princess!

1
Does Sofia look happy?

Yes | No

2
Use your finger to follow the magical trail and see who it leads to.

3

Clover and Whatnaught have crept in to watch all the fun. Can you find them?

4

Point to the three fairies.

Answers: 1) Yes. **2)** Flora. **3)** Clover is behind Amber and Whatnaught is next to Queen Miranda.

Princess Fun

Amber is showing Sofia her new princess things. They are going to play a memory game and you can play, too!

Below are 8 princess items. Look at them
for 10 seconds then cover them up. How
many can you remember?

I remembered _____ items.

Meet Mia
the Bluebird

Mia brightens up the castle gardens with her pretty songs and bubbly nature.

Sweet songbird

Beautiful Mia is a sweet, young songbird.

Kind heart

Mia is the kindest creature in the forest, so everyone loves her!

1

This word describes Mia. Trace over the letters so you can read it.

kind

2

Mia will look lovely if you colour her in.

Mia says:
I like Sofia because she tries very hard to be a good princess.

Shadow Game

Can you work out which shadow belongs to which character? Which shadow is left over?

Robin

Whatnaught

Clover

Mia

a

b

c

d

e

54

Answers: 1) a - Clover, c - Mia, d - Whatnaught, e - Robin. Shadow b is left, which is Sofia.

A princess is graceful and gracious.

✂ Cut along here.

It's Quiz Time!

Try this quiz and find out how much you know about Sofia and her world!

Tick the right answer.

1 Sofia's new best friend is:

a. Clover the Rabbit

b. James

c. Cedric the Sorcerer

2 Where does Sofia go to school?

a. In the castle

b. Royal Prep Academy

c. Enchancia Park School

3 What is Sofia's magical power?

a. She can become invisible

b. Her hair can change colour

c. She can talk to animals

Turn the page for more.

4 Sofia's new dad is a:

a. King

b. Prince

c. Farmer

5 What would Sofia choose to do?

a. Some homework

b. Have an adventure

c. Clean her bedroom

6 A good princess must be:

a. Graceful and lazy

b. Kind and greedy

c. Sweet and loving

Now, check the answers and see how much of a Sofia expert you are!

Best princess
friend ever! Add a
royal finish with your
colouring pens.

£5.99

Disney
DOC
McStuffins

Holiday Annual

EGMONT

Packed with stories

Puzzles & activities

Pretty stickers inside!